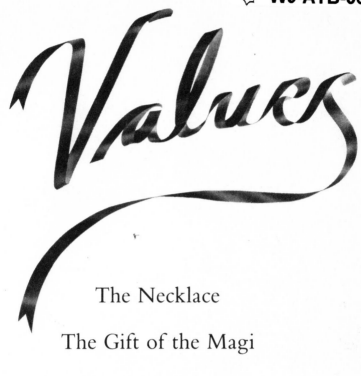

Values

The Necklace

The Gift of the Magi

This Farm for Sale

Assembly Line

HOUGHTON MIFFLIN COMPANY BOSTON

Atlanta   Dallas   Geneva, Illinois   Palo Alto   Princeton   Toronto

Acknowledgments

"The Necklace," from Guy de Maupassant: *The Mountain Inn and Other Stories* translated by H. N. P. Sloman (Penguin Classics, 1955), translation copyright © H. N. P. Sloman, 1955. Reprinted by permission of Penguin Books, Ltd.

Excerpts from "This Farm for Sale" by Jesse Stuart from *The Best-Loved Stories of Jesse Stuart,* edited by H. E. Richardson. Copyright © 1982. Used with permission of the Jesse Stuart Foundation, Judy B. Thomas, Chair, P.O. Box 391, Ashland, KY 41114. H. E. Richardson, Editor-in-Chief, Department of English, University of Louisville, Louisville, KY 40292.

"The Road Not Taken," by Robert Frost, copyright 1916, © 1969 by Holt, Rinehart & Winston. Copyright 1944 by Robert Frost. Reprinted from *The Poetry of Robert Frost* edited by Edward Connery Lathem, by permission of Henry Holt and Company, Inc.

"Assembly Line" from *The Night Visitor and Other Stories* by B. Traven. Copyright © 1966 by B. Traven. All rights reserved. Reprinted by permission of Farrar, Straus & Giroux, Inc. 19 Union Square West, New York, N.Y. 10003.

Credits

Cover Illustration John Mattos.

Illustration Shelley Freshman Austin: pp. 13, 27, 42, 58.

Photography AP/World Wide Photos: pp. 78L, 80.
Historical Pictures Service: p. 77.

Printed in the U.S.A.

ISBN: 0-395-45995-8

DEFGHIJ-B-976543210/89

Values are relative—that is, they differ among people. What one person considers valuable, another may not. People place value on things and on other people for a variety of reasons.

A necklace, a watch, a head of hair, a farm, and a basket—what do these objects have in common? How could the loss of any of these items significantly change the lives of the people in the following short stories?

Table of Contents

THE NECKLACE

BY *GUY* DE *MAUPASSANT*

S HE WAS ONE of those attractive pretty girls, born by a freak of fortune in a lower-middle-class family. She had no dowry, no expectations, no way of getting known, appreciated, loved and married by some wealthy gentleman of good family. And she allowed herself to be married to a junior clerk in the Ministry of Public Instruction.

She dressed plainly, having no money to spend on herself. But she was as unhappy as if she had known better days. Women have no sense of caste or breeding, their beauty, their grace, and their charm taking the place of birth and family. Their natural refinement, their instinctive delicacy and adaptability are their only passport to society, and these qualities enable daughters of the people to compete with ladies of gentle birth.

She always had a sense of frustration, feeling herself born for all the refinements and luxuries of life. She hated the bareness of her apartment, the shabbiness of the walls, the worn upholstery of the chairs, and the ugliness of the curtains. All these things, which another woman of her class would not even have noticed, were pain and grief to her. The sight of the little Breton maid doing her simple housework aroused in her passionate regrets and hopeless dreams. She imagined hushed anterooms hung with oriental fabrics and lit by tall bronze candelabra, with two impressive footmen in knee breeches dozing in great armchairs, made drowsy by the heat of radiators. She imagined vast drawing rooms, upholstered in antique silk, splendid pieces of furniture littered with priceless curios, and dainty scented boudoirs, designed for teatime conversation with intimate friends and much sought-after society gentlemen, whose attentions every woman envies and desires.

When she sat down to dinner at the round table covered with a three-days-old cloth opposite her husband, who took the lid off the casserole with the delighted exclamation: "Ah! your good stew again! How lovely! It's the best dish in the world!" she was dreaming of luxurious dinners with gleaming silver and tapestries peopling the walls with classical figures and exotic birds in a fairy forest; she dreamed of exquisite dishes served on valuable china and whispered compliments listened to with a sphinxlike smile, while toying with the pink flesh of a trout or the wing of a hazel-hen.

She had no evening clothes, no jewels, nothing. But she wanted only those things; she felt that that was the kind of life for her. She so much longed to please, be envied, be fascinating and sought after.

She had a rich friend who had been with her at a convent school, but she did not like going to see her now, the contrast was so painful when she went home. She spent whole days in tears; misery, regrets, hopeless longings caused her such bitter distress.

One evening her husband came home with a broad smile on his face and a large envelope in his hand: "Look!" he cried. "Here's something for you, dear!"

She tore open the envelope eagerly and pulled out a

printed card with the words: "The Minister of Public Instruction and Mme. Georges Ramponneau request the honor of the company of M. and Mme. Loisel[1] at the Ministry on the evening of Monday, January 18th."

Instead of being delighted as her husband had hoped, she threw the invitation pettishly down on the table, murmuring: "What's the good of this to me?"

"But I thought you'd be pleased, dear! You never go out and this is an occasion, a great occasion. I had the greatest difficulty to get the invitation. Everybody wants one; it's very select and junior clerks don't often get asked. The whole official world will be there."

She looked at him crossly and declared impatiently: "What do you think I'm to wear?"

He hadn't thought of that and stuttered: "Why! the frock you wear for the theater. I think it's charming!"

He stopped in astonished bewilderment when he saw his wife was crying. Two great tears were running slowly down from the corners of her eyes to the corners of her mouth; he stammered: "What's the matter? What's the matter?"

But with a great effort she had controlled her disappointment and replied quietly, drying her wet cheeks: "Oh! Nothing! Only not having anything to wear I can't go to the party. Pass on the invitation to some colleague whose wife is better dressed than I."

"Look here, Mathilde! How much would a suitable frock cost, something quite simple that would be useful on other occasions later on?"

She thought for a few seconds, doing a sum and also wondering how much she could ask for without inviting

---

[1] *Loisel:* pronounced lwä zĕl'.

an immediate refusal and an outraged exclamation from the close-fisted clerk. At last with some hesitation she replied: "I don't know exactly but I think I could manage on four hundred francs."

He went slightly pale, for this was just the amount he had put by to get a gun so that he could enjoy some shooting the following summer on the Nanterre plain with some friends who went out lark-shooting on Sundays. But he said: "Right! I'll give you four hundred francs, but try and get a really nice frock."

The date of the party was approaching and Mme. Loisel seemed depressed and worried, though her dress was ready. One evening her husband said to her: "What's the matter? The last three days you've not been yourself."

She replied: "It's rotten not to have a piece of jewelry, not a stone of any kind, to wear. I shall look poverty-stricken. I'd rather not go to the party."

He answered: "But you can wear some real flowers. That's very smart this year. For ten francs you could get two or three magnificent roses."

She was not impressed. "No, there's nothing more humiliating than to look poor in a crowd of wealthy women."

But her husband suddenly cried: "What a fool you are! Go to your friend, Mme. Forestier,[2] and ask her to lend you some of her jewelry. You know her well enough to do that."

She uttered a joyful cry: "That's a good idea! I'd never thought of it!"

Next day she went to her friend's house and explained her dilemma.

Mme. Forestier went to a glass-fronted wardrobe, took

---

[2] *Forestier:* pronounced fô rĕs tē ā'.

out a large casket, brought it over, opened it, and said to Mme. Loisel:

"Take what you like, my dear!"

First she looked at bracelets, then a pearl collar, then a Venetian cross in gold and stones, a lovely piece of work. She tried the various ornaments in front of the mirror, unable to make up her mind to take them off and put them back; she kept asking: "Haven't you got anything else?"

"Yes, go on looking; I don't know what you would like."

Suddenly she found a black satin case containing a magnificent diamond necklace, and she wanted it so desperately that her heart began to thump. Her hands were shaking as she picked it up. She put it round her throat over her high blouse and stood in ecstasy before her reflection in the glass. Then she asked hesitantly, her anxiety showing in her voice: "Could you lend me that, just that, nothing else?"

"But of course!"

She threw her arms round her friend's neck and kissed her wildly, and hurried home with her treasure.

The day of the party arrived. Mme. Loisel had a triumph. She was the prettiest woman in the room, elegant, graceful, smiling, in the seventh heaven of happiness. All the men looked at her, asked who she was, and wanted to be introduced. All the private secretaries wanted to dance with her. The Minister himself noticed her.

She danced with inspired abandon, intoxicated with delight, thinking of nothing in the triumph of her beauty and the glory of her success; she was wrapped in a cloud of happiness, the result of all the compliments, all the admiration, all these awakened desires, that wonderful success so dear to every woman's heart.

She left about four in the morning. Her husband had

been dozing since midnight in a small, empty drawing room with three other gentlemen, whose wives were also enjoying themselves.

He threw over her shoulders the wraps he had brought for going home, her simple everyday coat, whose plainness clashed with the smartness of her ball dress. She was conscious of this and wanted to hurry away, so as not to be noticed by the ladies who were putting on expensive fur wraps.

Loisel tried to stop her: "Wait a minute! You'll catch cold outside. I'll call a cab."

But she would not listen and ran down the stairs. When they got into the street they could not find a cab and began to hunt for one, shouting to the drivers they saw passing in the distance. In despair they went down towards the Seine, shivering. At last, on the Embankment they found one of those old carriages that ply by night and are only seen in Paris after dark, as if ashamed of their shabbiness in the daytime. It took them back to their house in the Rue des Martyrs and they went sadly up to their apartment. For her this was the end; and he was remembering that he had got to be at the office at ten o'clock.

She took off the wraps she had put round her shoulders, standing in front of the glass to see herself once more in all her glory. But suddenly she uttered a cry; the diamond necklace was no longer round her neck. Her husband, already half undressed, asked: "What's the matter?"

She turned to him in a panic: "Mme. Forestier's necklace has gone!"

He stood up, dumfounded: "What? What do you mean? It's impossible!"

They searched in the folds of her dress, in the folds of

her cloak, in the pockets, everywhere; they could not find it. He asked: "Are you sure you had it on when you left the ball?"

"Yes, I fingered it in the hall at the Ministry."

"But, if you had lost it in the street, we should have heard it drop. It must be in the cab."

"Yes, it probably is. Did you take the number?"

"No! And you didn't notice it, I suppose?"

"No!"

They looked at each other, utterly crushed. Finally Loisel dressed again: "I'll go back along the way we walked and see if I can find it."

He went out and she remained in her evening dress, without the strength even to go to bed, collapsed on a chair, without a fire, her mind a blank.

Her husband returned about seven, having found nothing. He went to the police station, to the papers to offer a reward, to the cab companies, in fact anywhere that gave a flicker of hope.

She waited all day in the same state of dismay at this appalling catastrophe. Loisel came back in the evening, his face pale and lined; he had discovered nothing.

"You must write to your friend," he said, "and say you have broken the clasp of the necklace and are getting it mended. That will give us time to turn around."

So she wrote at his dictation. After a week they had lost all hope and Loisel, who had aged five years, declared: "We must do something about replacing it."

Next day they took the case which had contained the necklace to the jeweler whose name was in it. He looked up his books: "I did not sell the jewel, Madame; I must only have supplied the case."

They went from jeweler to jeweler, looking for a necklace like the other, trying to remember exactly what it was like, both of them sick with worry and anxiety.

At last in the Palais Royal they found a diamond necklace just like the one lost. Its price was forty thousand francs, but they could have it for thirty-six thousand.

So they asked the jeweler to keep it for three days. They made it a condition that he should take it back for thirty-four thousand if the first was found before the end of February.

Loisel had got eighteen thousand francs which his father had left him; he would borrow the rest.

He borrowed one thousand francs from one, five hundred from another, one hundred here, sixty there. He gave I.O.U.'s and notes of hand on ruinous terms, going to the loan sharks and moneylenders of every kind. He mortgaged the whole of the rest of his life, risked his signature on bills without knowing if he would ever be able to honor it; he was tormented with anxiety about the future, with the thought of the crushing poverty about to descend upon him and the prospect of physical privations and mental agony. Then he went and collected the necklace, putting down the thirty-six thousand francs on the jeweler's counter.

When Mme. Loisel took the necklace back to Mme. Forestier, the latter said rather coldly: "You ought to have brought it back sooner; I might have wanted it."

She did not open the case, as her friend had feared she might. If she had detected the replacement what would she have thought? What would she have said? Would she have considered her a thief?

Now Mme. Loisel learned to know the grim life of the very poor. However, she faced the position with heroic courage. This ghastly debt must be paid and she would pay it. They got rid of the maid; they gave up the apartment and took an attic under the tiles. She did all the heavy work of the house as well as the hateful kitchen jobs. She washed up, ruining her pink nails on the coarse crockery and the bottoms of the saucepans. She washed the dirty linen and shirts and the kitchen cloths and dried them on a line. She carried the rubbish down to the street every morning and brought up the water, stopping on every floor to get her breath. And dressed as a woman of the people, she went to the fruiterer, the grocer and the butcher with her basket on her arm, bargaining in spite of their rudeness and fighting for every penny of her miserable pittance.

Every month some notes of hand had to be paid off and others renewed to gain time. Her husband worked in the evening keeping a tradesman's books and often at night he did copying at twenty-five centimes a page. This life went on for ten years.

After ten years they had paid everything back, including the interest and the accumulated compound interest.

Mme. Loisel now looked an old woman. She had become the strong, tough, coarse woman we find in the homes of the poor. Her hair was neglected, her skirt was askew, her hands were red, and her voice loud; she even scrubbed the floors. But sometimes, when her husband was at the office, she would sit down near the window and dream of that evening long ago, the ball at which she had been such a success.

What would have happened to her if she had not lost the necklace? Who can say? Life is such a strange thing with its changes and chances. Such a little thing can make or mar it!

One Sunday, when she had gone for a stroll in the Champs-Élysées as a change from the week's grind, she suddenly saw a lady taking a child for a walk. It was Mme. Forestier, still young, still beautiful, still attractive.

Mme. Loisel felt a wave of emotion. Should she speak to her? Yes, she would. Now that she had paid, she would tell her everything. Why not?

She went up to her: "Good morning, Jeanne!"

The other woman did not recognize her; surprised at being addressed in this familiar fashion by a common woman, she stammered: "But, Madame . . . I don't know you . . . there must be some mistake."

"No! I'm Mathilde Loisel!"

Her friend exclaimed: "Oh! Poor Mathilde, how you've changed!"

"Yes, I've had a pretty grim time since I saw you last, with lots of trouble—and it was all your fault!"

"My fault? What do you mean?"

"You remember that diamond necklace you lent me to go to the party at the Ministry?"

"Yes, what about it?"

"Well! I lost it!"

"What! But you brought it back to me."

"I brought you back another exactly like it; and for ten years we've been paying for it. You'll realize it hasn't been easy, for we had no money of our own. Well, now it's all over and I'm glad of it!"

Mme. Forestier had stopped: "You say you bought a diamond necklace to replace mine?"

"Yes! And you never spotted it, did you? They were as like as two peas."

And she smiled with simple proud pleasure.

Mme. Forestier, deeply moved, took both her hands: "Oh! my poor Mathilde! But mine was only paste, not worth more than five hundred francs at most!"

Discussion

1. What might have been Mathilde's feelings when she learned that the necklace was "only paste, not worth more than five hundred francs at most"?

2. Would Mathilde have been truly happy if she had been able to live the life she dreamed about? Explain your answer.

3. Do you think M. Loisel shared Mathilde's aspirations for a grander life? Explain your answer.

4. What do you think would have happened to Mathilde if she had not lost the necklace?

The Gift
of the Magi

THE GIFT
OF THE MAGI

BY O. HENRY

*O*NE DOLLAR and eighty-seven cents. That was all. And sixty cents of it was in pennies. Pennies saved one and two at a time by bulldozing the grocer and the vegetable man and the butcher until one's cheeks burned with the silent imputation of parsimony that such close dealing implied. Three times Della counted it. One dollar and eighty-seven cents. And the next day would be Christmas.

There was clearly nothing to do but flop down on the shabby little couch and howl. So Della did it. Which instigates the moral reflection that life is made up of sobs, sniffles, and smiles, with sniffles predominating.

While the mistress of the home is gradually subsiding from the first stage to the second, take a look at the home. A furnished flat at $8 per week. It did not exactly beggar description, but it certainly had that word on the lookout for the mendicancy squad.

In the vestibule below was a letter-box into which no letter would go, and an electric button from which no mortal finger could coax a ring. Also appertaining thereunto was a card bearing the name "Mr. James Dillingham Young."

The "Dillingham" had been flung to the breeze during a former period of prosperity when its possessor was being paid $30 per week. Now, when the income was shrunk to

$20, the letters of "Dillingham" looked blurred, as though they were thinking seriously of contracting to a modest and unassuming D. But whenever Mr. James Dillingham Young came home and reached his flat above he was called "Jim" and greatly hugged by Mrs. James Dillingham Young, already introduced to you as Della. Which is all very good.

Della finished her cry and attended to her cheeks with the powder rag. She stood by the window and looked out dully at a gray cat walking a gray fence in a gray backyard. Tomorrow would be Christmas Day, and she had only $1.87 with which to buy Jim a present. She had been saving every penny she could for months, with this result. Twenty dollars a week doesn't go far. Expenses had been greater than she had calculated. They always are. Only $1.87 to buy a present for Jim. Her Jim. Many a happy hour she had spent planning for something nice for him. Something fine and rare and sterling—something just a little bit near to being worthy of the honor of being owned by Jim.

There was a pier-glass between the windows of the room. Perhaps you have seen a pier-glass in an $8 flat. A very thin and very agile person may, by observing his reflection in a rapid sequence of longitudinal strips, obtain a fairly accurate conception of his looks. Della, being slender, had mastered the art.

Suddenly she whirled from the window and stood before the glass. Her eyes were shining brilliantly, but her face had lost its color within twenty seconds. Rapidly she pulled down her hair and let it fall to its full length.

Now, there were two possessions of the James Dillingham Youngs in which they both took a mighty pride. One was Jim's gold watch that had been his father's and his grandfather's. The other was Della's hair. Had the Queen of Sheba lived in the flat across the airshaft, Della would have let her hair hang out the window some day to dry just to depreciate Her Majesty's jewels and gifts. Had King Solomon been the janitor, with all his treasures piled up in the basement, Jim would have pulled out his watch every time he passed, just to see him pluck at his beard from envy.

So now Della's beautiful hair fell about her, rippling and shining like a cascade of brown waters. It reached below her knee and made itself almost a garment for her. And then she did it up again nervously and quickly. Once she faltered for a minute and stood still while a tear or two splashed on the worn red carpet.

On went her old brown jacket; on went her old brown hat. With a whirl of skirts and with the brilliant sparkle still in her eyes, she fluttered out the door and down the stairs to the street.

Where she stopped the sign read: "Mme. Sofronie. Hair Goods of All Kinds." One flight up Della ran, and collected herself, panting. Madame, large, too white, chilly, hardly looked the "Sofronie."

"Will you buy my hair?" asked Della.

"I buy hair," said Madame. "Take yer hat off and let's have a sight at the looks of it."

Down rippled the brown cascade.

"Twenty dollars," said Madame, lifting the mass with a practiced hand.

"Give it to me quick," said Della.

Oh, and the next two hours tripped by on rosy wings. Forget the hashed metaphor. She was ransacking the stores for Jim's present.

She found it at last. It surely had been made for Jim and no one else. There was no other like it in any of the stores, and she had turned all of them inside out. It was a platinum fob chain simple and chaste in design, properly

proclaiming its value by substance alone and not by meretricious ornamentation—as all good things should do. It was even worthy of The Watch. As soon as she saw it she knew that it must be Jim's. It was like him. Quietness and value—the description applied to both. Twenty-one dollars they took from her for it, and she hurried home with the 87 cents. With that chain on his watch Jim might be properly anxious about the time in any company. Grand as the watch was, he sometimes looked at it on the sly on account of the old leather strap that he used in place of a chain.

When Della reached home her intoxication gave way a little to prudence and reason. She got out her curling irons and lighted the gas and went to work repairing the ravages made by generosity added to love. Which is always a tremendous task, dear friends—a mammoth task.

Within forty minutes her head was covered with tiny, close-lying curls that made her look wonderfully like a truant schoolboy. She looked at her reflection in the mirror long, carefully, and critically.

"If Jim doesn't kill me," she said to herself, "before he takes a second look at me, he'll say I look like a Coney Island chorus girl. But what could I do—oh! what could I do with a dollar and eighty-seven cents?"

At 7 o'clock the coffee was made and the frying-pan was on the back of the stove hot and ready to cook the chops.

Jim was never late. Della doubled the fob chain in her hand and sat on the corner of the table near the door that he always entered. Then she heard his step on the stair away down on the first flight, and she turned white for just a moment. She had a habit of saying little silent prayers about the simplest everyday things, and now she whispered: "Please God, make him think I am still pretty."

The door opened and Jim stepped in and closed it. He

looked thin and very serious. Poor fellow, he was only twenty-two—and to be burdened with a family! He needed a new overcoat and he was without gloves.

Jim stopped inside the door, as immovable as a setter at the scent of quail. His eyes were fixed upon Della, and there was an expression in them that she could not read, and it terrified her. It was not anger, nor surprise, nor disapproval, nor horror, nor any of the sentiments that she had been prepared for. He simply stared at her fixedly with that peculiar expression on his face.

Della wriggled off the table and went for him.

"Jim, darling," she cried, "don't look at me that way. I had my hair cut off and sold it because I couldn't have lived through Christmas without giving you a present. It'll grow out again—you won't mind, will you? I just had to do it. My hair grows awfully fast. Say 'Merry Christmas!' Jim, and let's be happy. You don't know what a nice—what a beautiful, nice gift I've got for you."

"You've cut off your hair?" asked Jim, laboriously, as if he had not arrived at that patent fact yet even after the hardest mental labor.

"Cut it off and sold it," said Della. "Don't you like me just as well, anyhow? I'm me without my hair, ain't I?"

Jim looked about the room curiously.

"You say your hair is gone?" he said, with an air almost of idiocy.

"You needn't look for it," said Della. "It's sold, I tell you—sold and gone, too. It's Christmas Eve, boy. Be good to me, for it went for you. Maybe the hairs of my head were numbered," she went on with a sudden serious sweetness, "but nobody could ever count my love for you. Shall I put the chops on, Jim?"

Out of his trance Jim seemed quickly to wake. He enfolded

his Della. For ten seconds let us regard with discreet scrutiny some inconsequential object in the other direction. Eight dollars a week or a million a year—what is the difference? A mathematician or a wit would give you the wrong answer. The magi brought valuable gifts, but that was not among them. This dark assertion will be illuminated later on.

Jim drew a package from his overcoat pocket and threw it upon the table.

"Don't make any mistake, Dell," he said, "about me. I don't think there's anything in the way of a haircut or a shave or a shampoo that could make me like my girl any less. But if you'll unwrap that package you may see why you had me going a while at first."

White fingers and nimble tore at the string and paper. And then an ecstatic scream of joy; and then, alas! a quick feminine change to hysterical tears and wails, necessitating the immediate employment of all the comforting powers of the lord of the flat.

For there lay The Combs—the set of combs, side and back, that Della had worshipped for long in a Broadway window. Beautiful combs, pure tortoise shell, with jewelled rims—just the shade to wear in the beautiful vanished hair. They were expensive combs, she knew, and her heart had simply craved and yearned over them without the least hope of possession. And now, they were hers, but the tresses that should have adorned the coveted adornments were gone.

But she hugged them to her bosom, and at length she was able to look up with dim eyes and a smile and say: "My hair grows so fast, Jim!"

And then Della leaped up like a little singed cat and cried, "Oh, oh!"

Jim had not yet seen his beautiful present. She held it

out to him eagerly upon her open palm. The dull precious metal seemed to flash with a reflection of her bright and ardent spirit.

"Isn't it a dandy, Jim? I hunted all over town to find it. You'll have to look at the time a hundred times a day now. Give me your watch. I want to see how it looks on it."

Instead of obeying, Jim tumbled down on the couch and put his hands under the back of his head and smiled.

"Dell," said he, "let's put our Christmas presents away and keep 'em a while. They're too nice to use just at present. I sold the watch to get the money to buy your combs. And now suppose you put the chops on."

The magi, as you know, were wise men—wonderfully wise men—who brought gifts to the Babe in the manger. They invented the art of giving Christmas presents. Being wise, their gifts were no doubt wise ones, possibly bearing the privilege of exchange in case of duplication. And here I have lamely related to you the uneventful chronicle of two foolish children in a flat who most unwisely sacrificed for each other the greatest treasures of their house. But in a last word to the wise of these days let it be said that of all who give gifts these two were the wisest. Of all who give and receive gifts, such as they are wisest. Everywhere they are wisest. They are the magi.

Discussion

1. Della and Jim both have the gifts they wanted. What do you think they will do with their gifts now?

2. The author says, ". . . let it be said that of all who give gifts these two were the wisest." What does he mean? Do you agree?

3. Della and Jim probably valued their gifts more because they knew of the great sacrifice each had made. If someone made a great sacrifice to give you something you really wanted, would you want to know about that sacrifice? Explain your answer.

This
Farm for Sale

THIS
FARM FOR SALE

BY JESSE STUART

*T*HIS TIME we're goin' to sell this farm," Uncle Dick said to Aunt Emma. "I've just learned how to sell a farm. Funny, I never thought of it myself."

My cousins—Olive, Helen, Oliver, and Little Dick—all stopped eating and looked at one another and then looked at Uncle Dick and Aunt Emma. When Aunt Emma smiled, they smiled, too. Everybody seemed happy because Uncle Dick, who had just come from Blakesburg, had found a way to sell the farm. Everybody was happy but me. I was sorry Uncle Dick was going to sell the farm.

"This farm is just as good as sold!" Uncle Dick talked on. "I've got a real estate man, my old friend Melvin Spencer, coming here tomorrow to look the place over. He's goin' to sell it for me."

"I'd like to get enough for it to make a big payment on a fine house in Blakesburg," Aunt Emma said. "I've got the one picked out that I want. It's the beautiful Coswell house. I understand it's up for sale now and no one's livin' in it!"

"Gee, that will be wonderful," Cousin Olive said. "Right on the street and not any mud. We wouldn't have to wear galoshes all winter if we lived there!"

"I'll say it will be wonderful," Helen said, with a smile. "Daddy, I hope Mr. Spencer can sell this place."

I wanted to tell Aunt Emma the reason why no one was living in the Coswell house. Every time Big River rose to flood stage, the water got on the first floor in the house; and this was the reason why the Coswells had built a house on higher ground outside Blakesburg and had moved to it. And this was the reason why they couldn't keep a renter any longer than it took Big River to rise to flood stage. But this wasn't my business, so I didn't say anything.

"Mel Spencer will come here to look this farm over," Uncle Dick said, puffing on his cigar until he'd almost filled the dining room with smoke. "Then he'll put an ad in the *Blakesburg Gazette.*"

"What will we do about the cows, horses, hogs, honeybees, hay in the barn lofts and in the stacks, and corn in the bins?" Cousin Oliver asked.

"Sell them, too," Uncle Dick said. "When we sell, let's sell everything we have but our house plunder."

It was ten o'clock the next day before Melvin Spencer came. Since he couldn't drive his car all the way to Uncle Dick's farm, he rode the mail truck to Red Hot. Red Hot is a store and post office on the Tiber River. And at Red Hot, Uncle Dick met him with an extra horse and empty saddle. So Melvin Spencer came riding up with Uncle Dick. And I'll never forget the first words he said when he climbed down from the saddle.

"Richard, it's a great experience to be in the saddle again," he said, breathing deeply of the fresh air. "All this reminds me of another day and time."

Oliver, Little Dick, and I followed Melvin Spencer and Uncle Dick as they started walking toward the Tiber bottoms.

"How many acres in this farm, Richard?" Melvin Spencer asked.

"The deed calls for three hundred, more or less," Uncle Dick said.

"How many acres of bottom land?" he asked Uncle Dick.

"I'd say about sixty-five," Uncle Dick replied.

We walked down the jolt-wagon road, where my cousins and I had often ridden Nell and Jerry to and from the field.

"What kind of land is this?" Melvin Spencer asked. He had to look up to see the bright heads of cane.

"It's limestone land," Uncle Dick bragged. "Never had to use fertilizer. My people have farmed these bottoms over a hundred years."

Then Uncle Dick showed Melvin Spencer the corn we had laid by. It was August, and our growing corn was maturing. Melvin Spencer looked at the big cornfield. He was very silent. We walked on to the five acres of tobacco, where the broad leaves crossed the balks[1] and a man couldn't walk through. Then we went down to the river.

"My farm comes to this river," Uncle Dick said. "I've often thought what a difference it would be if we had a bridge across this river. Then I could reach the Tiber road and go east to Blakesburg and west to Darter City. But we don't have a bridge; and until we go down the river seven miles to Red Hot where we can cross to the Tiber road, we'll always be in the mud. I've heard all my life that the county would build a bridge. My father heard it, too, in his lifetime."

"You *are* shut in here," Melvin Spencer agreed, as he looked beyond the Tiber River at the road.

"Now, we'll go to the house and get some dinner," Uncle

---

[1] *balks:* ridges of land left unploughed.

Dick said. "Then I'll take you up on the hill this afternoon and show you my timber and the rest of the farm."

When we reached the big house, Melvin Spencer stopped for a minute and looked at the house and yard.

"You know, when I sell a piece of property, I want to look it over," he told Uncle Dick. "I want to know all about it. How old is this house?"

"The date was cut on the chimney," Uncle Dick said.

Melvin Spencer looked over the big squat log house with the plank door, big stone steps, small windows, the moss-covered roof. Then we went inside, and he started looking again. That is, he did until Uncle Dick introduced him to Aunt Emma and Aunt Emma introduced him to a table that made him stand and look some more.

"I've never seen anything like this since I was a boy," Melvin Spencer said, showing more interest in the loaded table than he had in the farm.

"All of this came from our farm here," Uncle Dick said.

I never saw a man eat like Melvin Spencer. He ate like I did when I first came to Uncle Dick's and Aunt Emma's each spring when school was over. He tried to eat something of everything on the table, but he couldn't get around to it all.

"If I could sell this farm like you can prepare a meal, I'd get a whopping big price for it," he said with a chuckle as he looked at Aunt Emma.

"I hope you can," Aunt Emma said. "We're too far back here. Our children have to wade the winter mud to get to school. And we don't have electricity. We don't have the things that city people have. And I think every country woman wants them."

Melvin Spencer didn't listen to all that Aunt Emma said. He was much too busy eating. And long before he had

finished, Uncle Dick pulled a cigar from his inside coat pocket, struck a match under the table, lit it, and blew a big cloud of smoke toward the ceiling in evident enjoyment.

He looked at Aunt Emma and smiled.

"The old place is as good as sold, Mother," Uncle Dick said with a wink. "You're a-goin' to be out of the mud. We'll let some other woman slave around here and wear galoshes all winter. We'll be on the bright, clean streets wearin' well-shined shoes—every blessed one of us. We'll have an electric washer, a radio where we won't have to have the batteries charged, a bathroom, and an electric stove. No more of this stove-wood choppin' for the boys and me."

When Uncle Dick said this, Olive and Helen looked at Aunt Emma and smiled. I looked at Oliver and Little Dick, and they were grinning. But Melvin Spencer never looked up from his plate.

When we got up from the table, Melvin Spencer thanked Aunt Emma, Cousin Olive, and Helen for the "best dinner" he'd had since he was a young man. Then he asked Aunt Emma for a picture of the house.

Aunt Emma sent Helen to get it. "If you can, just sell this place for us," Aunt Emma said to Melvin Spencer.

"I'll do my best," he promised her. "But as you ought to know, it will be a hard place to sell, located way back here and without a road."

"Are you a-goin' to put a picture of this old house in the paper?" Uncle Dick asked, as Helen came running with the picture.

"I might," Melvin Spencer said. "I never say much in an ad, since I have to make my words count. A picture means a sale sometimes. Of course, this expense will come from the sale of the property."

He said good-by to Aunt Emma, Olive, and Helen. Little Dick, Oliver, and I followed him and Uncle Dick out of the house and up the hill where the yellow poplars and the pines grow.

"Why hasn't this timber been cut long ago?" Melvin Spencer asked, looking up at the trees.

"Not any way to haul it out," Uncle Dick told him.

"That's right," Melvin Spencer said. "I'd forgot about the road. If a body doesn't have a road to his farm, Richard, he's not got much of a place."

"These old trees get hollow and blow down in storms," Uncle Dick said. "They should have been cut down a long time ago."

"Yes, they should have," Melvin Spencer agreed, as he put his hand on the bark of a yellow poplar. "We used to have trees like this in Pike County. But not any more."

While we walked under the beech grove, we came upon a drove of slender bacon hogs eating beechnuts.

"Old Skinny bacon hogs," Uncle Dick said, as they scurried past us. "They feed on the mast of the beeches and oaks, on saw-briar, greenbriar, and pine-tree roots, and on mulberries, persimmons, and pawpaws."

When we climbed to the top of a hill, the land slanted in all directions.

"Show me from here what you own," Melvin Spencer said.

"It's very easy, Mel," Uncle Dick said. "The stream on the right and the one on the left are the left and right forks of Wolfe Creek. They are boundary lines. I own all the land between them. I own all the bottom land from where the forks join, down to that big bend in the Tiber. And I own down where the Tiber flows against those white limestone cliffs."

"You are fenced in by natural boundaries," Melvin Spencer said. "They're almost impossible to cross. This place will be hard to sell, Richard."

Then we went back down the hill, and Melvin and Uncle Dick climbed into the saddles and were off down the little narrow road toward Red Hot. Their horses went away at a gallop, because Melvin Spencer had to catch the mail truck, and he was already behind schedule.

On Saturday, Uncle Dick rode to Red Hot to get the paper. Since he didn't read very well, he asked me to read what Melvin Spencer had said about his house. When I opened the paper and turned to the picture of the house, everybody gathered around.

"Think of a picture of this old house in the paper," Aunt Emma said.

"But there are pictures of other houses for sale in the paper," Uncle Dick told her. "That's not anything to crow about."

"But it's the best-looking of the four," Cousin Olive said.

"It does look better than I thought it would," Aunt Emma sighed.

"Look, here's two columns all the way down the page," I said. "The other four places advertised here have only a paragraph about them."

"Read it," Uncle Dick said. "I'd like to know what Mel said about this place. Something good, I hope."

So I read this aloud:

Yesterday, I had a unique experience when I visited the farm of Mr. and Mrs. Richard Stone, which they have asked me to sell. I cannot write an ad about this farm. I must tell you about it.

I went up a winding road on horseback. Hazelnut bushes, with clusters of green hazelnuts bending their slender stems, swished across my face. Pawpaws, heavy with green clusters of fruit, grew along this road. Persimmons with bending boughs covered one slope below the road. Here are wild fruits and nuts of Nature's cultivation for the one who possesses land like this. Not any work but just to go out and gather the fruit. How many of you city dwellers would love this?

"What about him a-mentionin' the persimmons, pawpaws, and hazelnuts!" Uncle Dick broke in. "I'd never have thought of them. They're common things!"

When we put the horses in the big barn, Mr. Stone, his two sons, his nephew, and I walked down into his Tiber-bottom farm land. And, like the soil along the Nile River, this overflowed land, rich with limestone, never has to be fertilized. I saw cane as high as a giraffe, and as dark green as the waves of the Atlantic. It grew in long, straight rows with brown clusters of seed that looked to be up against the blue of the sky. I have never seen such dark clouds of corn grow out of the earth. Five acres of tobacco, with leaves as broad as a mountaineer's shoulders. Pleasant meadows with giant haystacks here and there. It is a land rich with fertility and abundant with crops.

"That sounds wonderful," Aunt Emma said, smiling.

This peaceful Tiber River, flowing dreamily down the valley, is a boundary to his farm. Here one can see to the bottoms of the deep holes, the water is so clear and blue. One can catch fish from the river for his next meal. Elder bushes, where they gather the berries to make the finest jelly in the world, grow along this riverbank as thick as ragweeds. The Stones have farmed this land for four generations, have lived in the same house, have gathered elderberries for their jelly along the Tiber riverbanks, and fished in its sky-blue waters that long—and yet they will sell this land.

"Just a minute, Shan," Uncle Dick said as he got up from his chair. "Stop just a minute."

Uncle Dick pulled a handkerchief from his pocket and wiped the sweat from his forehead. His face seemed a bit flushed. He walked a little circle around the living room and then sat back down in his chair. But the sweat broke out on his face again when I started reading.

The proof of what a farm produces is at the farm table. I wish that whoever reads what I have written here could have seen the table prepared by Mrs. Stone and her two daughters. Hot fluffy biscuits with light-brown tops, brown-crusted cornbread, buttermilk, sweet milk (cooled in a free-stone well), wild-grape jelly, wild-crab-apple jelly, mast-fed lean bacon that melted in my mouth, fresh apple pie, wild-blackberry cobbler, honey-colored sorghum from the lime-stone bottoms of the Tiber, and wild honey from the beehives.

"Oh, no one ever said that about a meal I cooked before," Aunt Emma broke in.

"Just a minute, Shan," Uncle Dick said, as he got up from his chair and with his handkerchief in his hand again.

This time Uncle Dick went a bit faster as he circled the living room. He wiped sweat from his face as he walked. He had a worried look on his face. I read on:

Their house, eight rooms and two halls, would be a show place if close to some of our modern cities. The house itself would be worth the price I will later quote you on this farm. Giant yellow poplar logs with twenty- to thirty-inch facings, hewed smooth with broadaxes by the mighty hands of Stone pioneers, make the sturdy walls in this termite-proof house. Two planks make the broad doors in this house that is one-hundred-and-six years old. This beautiful home of pioneer architecture is without modern conveniences, but since a power line will be constructed up the Tiber

River early next spring, a few modern conveniences will be possible.

"I didn't know that!" Aunt Emma was excited. "I guess it's just talk, like about the bridge across the Tiber."

After lunch I climbed a high hill to look at the rest of this farm. I walked through a valley of virgin trees, where there were yellow poplars and pine sixty feet to the first limb. Beech trees with tops big enough to shade twenty-five head of cattle. Beechnuts streaming down like golden coins, to be gathered by the bacon hogs running wild. A farm with wild game and fowl, and a river bountiful with fish! And yet, this farm is for sale!

Uncle Dick walked over beside his chair. He looked as if he were going to fall over.

Go see for yourself roads not exploited by the county or state, where the horse's shoe makes music on the clay, where apple orchards with fruit are bending down, and barns and bins are full. Go see a way of life, a richness and fulfillment that make America great, that put solid foundation stones under America! This beautiful farm, fifty head of livestock, honeybees, crops old and new, and home for only $22,000!

"Oh!" Aunt Emma screamed. I thought she was going to faint. "Oh, he's killed it with that price. It's unheard of, Richard! You couldn't get $6000 for it."

Uncle Dick still paced the floor.

"What's the matter, Pa?" Oliver finally asked.

"I didn't know I had so much," Uncle Dick said. "I'm a rich man and didn't know it. I'm not selling this farm!"

"Don't worry, Richard," Aunt Emma said. "You won't sell it at that price!"

I never saw such disappointed looks as there were on my cousins' faces.

"But what will you do with Mr. Spencer?" Aunt Emma asked. "You've put the farm in his hands to sell."

"Pay him for his day and what he put in the paper," Uncle Dick told her. "I know we're not goin' to sell now, for it takes two to sign the deed. I'll be willing to pay Mel Spencer a little extra because he showed me what we have."

Then I laid the paper down and walked quietly from the room. Evening was coming on. I walked toward the meadows. I wanted to share the beauty of this farm with Melvin Spencer. I was never so happy.

Discussion

1. Shan did not tell his aunt and uncle what he knew about the Coswell house because he felt it was not his business to say anything. Was he right? Explain your answer.

2. Melvin Spencer does not want Uncle Dick to sell the farm. Why does he not simply say so?

3. What might have happened if some other real estate agent had looked over the farm?

4. After Shan read the newspaper description of the farm, Uncle Dick exclaimed, "I didn't know I had so much . . . I'm a rich man and didn't know it." Why is it only now that he knows the value of his farm?

Assembly Line

ASSEMBLY LINE

BY B. TRAVEN

*M*R. E. L. WINTHROP of New York was on vacation in the Republic of Mexico. It wasn't long before he realized that this strange and really wild country had not yet been fully and satisfactorily explored by Rotarians and Lions, who are forever conscious of their glorious mission on earth. Therefore, he considered it his duty as a good American citizen to do his part in correcting this oversight.

In search for opportunities to indulge in his new avocation, he left the beaten track and ventured into regions not especially mentioned, and hence not recommended, by travel agents to foreign tourists. So it happend that one day he found himself in a little, quaint Indian village somewhere in the State of Oaxaca.

Walking along the dusty main street of this pueblecito, which knew nothing of pavements, drainage, plumbing, or of any means of artificial light save candles or pine splinters, he met with an Indian squatting on the earthen-floor front porch of a palm hut, a so-called jacalito.

The Indian was busy making little baskets from bast and from all kinds of fibers gathered by him in the immense tropical bush which surrounded the village on all sides.

The material used had not only been well prepared for its purpose but was also richly colored with dyes that the basket-maker himself extracted from various native plants, barks, roots and from certain insects by a process known only to him and the members of his family.

His principal business, however, was not producing baskets. He was a peasant who lived on what the small property he possessed—less than fifteen acres of not too fertile soil—would yield, after much sweat and labor and after constantly worrying over the most wanted and best suited distribution of rain, sunshine, and wind and the changing balance of birds and insects beneficial or harmful to his crops. Baskets he made when there was nothing else for him to do in the fields, because he was unable to dawdle. After all, the sale of his baskets, though to a rather limited degree only, added to the small income he received from his little farm.

In spite of being by profession just a plain peasant, it was clearly seen from the small baskets he made that at heart he was an artist, a true and accomplished artist. Each basket looked as if covered all over with the most beautiful sometimes fantastic ornaments, flowers, butterflies, birds, squirrels, antelope, tigers, and a score of other animals of the wilds. Yet, the most amazing thing was that these decorations, all of them symphonies of color, were not painted on the baskets but were instead actually part of the baskets themselves. Bast and fibers dyed in dozens of different colors were so cleverly—one must actually say intrinsically—interwoven that those attractive designs appeared on the inner part of the basket as well as on the outside. Not by painting but by weaving were those highly artistic effects achieved. This performance he accomplished without ever looking at any sketch or pattern. While working on a basket these designs came to light as if by magic, and as long as a basket

was not entirely finished one could not perceive what in this case or that the decoration would be like.

People in the market town who bought these baskets would use them for sewing baskets or to decorate tables with or window sills, or to hold little things to keep them from lying around. Women put their jewelry in them or flowers or little dolls. There were in fact a hundred and two ways they might serve certain purposes in a household or in a lady's own room.

Whenever the Indian had finished about twenty of the baskets he took them to town on market day. Sometimes he would already be on his way shortly after midnight because he owned only a burro to ride on, and if the burro had gone astray the day before, as happened frequently, he would have to walk the whole way to town and back again.

At the market he had to pay twenty centavos in taxes to sell his wares. Each basket cost him between twenty and thirty hours of constant work, not counting the time spent gathering bast and fibers, preparing them, making dyes and coloring the bast. All this meant extra time and work. The price he asked for each basket was fifty centavos, the equivalent of about four cents. It seldom happened, however, that a buyer paid outright the full fifty centavos asked—or four reales as the Indian called that money. The prospective buyer started bargaining, telling the Indian that he ought to be ashamed to ask such a sinful price. "Why, the whole dirty thing is nothing but ordinary petate straw which you find in heaps wherever you may look for it; the jungle is packed full of it," the buyer would argue. "Such a little basket, what's it good for anyhow? If I paid you, you thief, ten centavitos for it you should be grateful and kiss my hand. Well, it's your lucky day, I'll be generous this time,

I'll pay you twenty, yet not one green centavo more. Take it or run along."

So he sold finally for twenty-five centavos, but then the buyer would say, "Now, what do you think of that? I've got only twenty centavos change on me. What can we do about that? If you can change me a twenty-peso bill, all right, you shall have your twenty-five fierros." Of course, the Indian could not change a twenty-peso bill and so the basket went for twenty centavos.

He had little if any knowledge of the outside world or he would have known that what happened to him was happening every hour of every day to every artist all over the world. That knowledge would perhaps have made him very proud, because he would have realized that he belonged to the little army which is the salt of the earth and which keeps culture, urbanity and beauty for their own sake from passing away.

Often it was not possible for him to sell all the baskets he had brought to market, for people here as elsewhere in the world preferred things made by the millions and each so much like the other that you were unable, even with the help of a magnifying glass, to tell which was which and where was the difference between two of the same kind.

Yet he, this craftsman, had in his life made several hundreds of those exquisite baskets, but so far no two of them had he ever turned out alike in design. Each was an individual piece of art and as different from the other as was a Murillo from a Velásquez.[1]

Naturally he did not want to take those baskets which

---

[1] *a Murillo . . . a Velásquez:* paintings by famous Spanish painters Bartolomé Esteban Murillo (1618–1682) and Diego Velásquez (1599–1660).

he could not sell at the market place home with him again if he could help it. In such a case he went peddling his products from door to door where he was treated partly as a beggar and partly as a vagrant apparently looking for an opportunity to steal, and he frequently had to swallow all sorts of insults and nasty remarks.

Then, after a long run, perhaps a woman would finally stop him, take one of the baskets and offer him ten centavos, which price through talks and talks would perhaps go up to fifteen or even to twenty. Nevertheless, in many instances he would actually get no more than just ten centavos, and the buyer, usually a woman, would grasp that little marvel and right before his eyes throw it carelessly upon the nearest table as if to say, "Well, I take that piece of nonsense only for charity's sake. I know my money is wasted. But then, after all, I'm a Christian and I can't see a poor Indian die of hunger since he has come such a long way from his village." This would remind her of something better and she would hold him and say, "Where are you at home anyway, Indito? What's your pueblo? So, from Huehuetonoc? Now, listen here, Indito, can't you bring me next Saturday two or three turkeys from Huehuetonoc? But they must be heavy and fat and very, very cheap or I won't even touch them. If I wish to pay the regular price I don't need you to bring them. Understand? Hop along, now, Indito."

The Indian squatted on the earthen floor in the portico of his hut, attended to his work and showed no special interest in the curiosity of Mr. Winthrop watching him. He acted almost as if he ignored the presence of the American altogether.

"How much that little basket, friend?" Mr. Winthrop asked when he felt that he at least had to say something as not to appear idiotic.

"Fifty centavitos, patroncito, my good little lordy, four reales," the Indian answered politely.

"All right, sold," Mr. Winthrop blurted out in a tone and with a wide gesture as if he had bought a whole railroad. And examining his buy he added, "I know already who I'll give that pretty little thing to. She'll kiss me for it, sure. Wonder what she'll use it for?"

He had expected to hear a price of three or even four pesos. The moment he realized that he had judged the value six times too high, he saw right away what great business possibilities this miserable Indian village might offer to a dynamic promoter like himself. Without further delay he started exploring those possibilities. "Suppose, my good friend, I buy ten of these little baskets of yours which, as I might as well admit right here and now, have practically no real use whatsoever. Well, as I was saying, if I buy ten, how much would you then charge me apiece?"

The Indian hesitated for a few seconds as if making calculations. Finally he said, "If you buy ten I can let you have them for forty-five centavos each, señorito gentleman."

"All right, amigo. And now, let's suppose I buy from you straight away one hundred of these absolutely useless baskets, how much will cost me each?"

The Indian, never fully looking up to the American standing before him and hardly taking his eyes off his work, said politely and without the slightest trace of enthusiasm in his voice, "In such a case I might not be quite unwilling to sell each for forty centavitos."

Mr. Winthrop bought sixteen baskets, which was all the Indian had in stock.

After three weeks' stay in the Republic, Mr. Winthrop was convinced that he knew this country perfectly, that he had seen everything and knew all about the inhabitants, their character and their way of life, and that there was nothing left for him to explore. So he returned to good old Nooyorg and felt happy to be once more in a civilized country, as he expressed it to himself.

One day going out for lunch he passed a confectioner's and, looking at the display in the window, he suddenly remembered the little baskets he had bought in that faraway Indian village.

He hurried home and took all the baskets he still had left to one of the best-known candy-makers in the city.

"I can offer you here," Mr. Winthrop said to the confectioner, "one of the most artistic and at the same time the most original of boxes, if you wish to call them that. These little baskets would be just right for the most expensive chocolates meant for elegant and high-priced gifts. Just have a good look at them, sir, and let me listen."

The confectioner examined the baskets and found them extraordinarily well suited for a certain line in his business. Never before had there been anything like them for originality, prettiness and good taste. He, however, avoided most carefully showing any sign of enthusiasm, for which there would be time enough once he knew the price and whether he could get a whole load exclusively.

He shrugged his shoulders and said, "Well, I don't know. If you asked me I'd say it isn't quite what I'm after. However, we might give it a try. It depends, of course, on the price. In our business the package mustn't cost more than what's in it."

"Do I hear an offer?" Mr. Winthrop asked.

"Why don't you tell me in round figures how much you want for them? I'm not good in guessing."

"Well, I'll tell you, Mr. Kemple: since I'm the smart guy

who discovered these baskets and since I'm the only Jack who knows where to lay his hands on more, I'm selling to the highest bidder, on an exclusive basis, of course. I'm positive you can see it my way, Mr. Kemple."

"Quite so, and may the best man win," the confectioner said. "I'll talk the matter over with my partners. See me tomorrow same time, please, and I'll let you know how far we might be willing to go."

Next day when both gentlemen met again Mr. Kemple said: "Now, to be frank with you, I know art on seeing it, no getting around that. And these baskets are little works of art, they surely are. However, we are no art dealers, you realize that of course. We've no other use for these pretty little things except as fancy packing for our French pralines made by us. We can't pay for them what we might pay considering them pieces of art. After all to us they're only wrappings. Fine wrappings, perhaps, but nevertheless wrappings. You'll see it our way I hope, Mr.——oh yes, Mr. Winthrop. So, here is our offer, take it or leave it: a dollar and a quarter apiece and not one cent more."

Mr. Winthrop made a gesture as if he had been struck over the head.

The confectioner, misunderstanding this involuntary gesture of Mr. Winthrop, added quickly, "All right, all right, no reason to get excited, no reason at all. Perhaps we can do a trifle better. Let's say one-fifty."

"Make it one-seventy-five," Mr. Winthrop snapped, swallowing his breath while wiping his forehead.

"Sold. One-seventy-five apiece free at port of New York. We pay the customs and you pay the shipping. Right?"

"Sold," Mr. Winthrop said also and the deal was closed.

"There is, of course, one condition," the confectioner explained just when Mr. Winthrop was to leave. "One or two hundred won't do for us. It wouldn't pay the trouble and the advertising. I won't consider less than ten thousand, or one thousand dozens if that sounds better in your ears. And they must come in no less than twelve different patterns well assorted. How about that?"

"I can make it sixty different patterns or designs."

"So much the better. And you're sure you can deliver ten thousand let's say early October?"

"Absolutely," Mr. Winthrop avowed and signed the contract.

Practically all the way back to Mexico, Mr. Winthrop had a notebook in his left hand and a pencil in his right and he was writing figures, long rows of them, to find out exactly how much richer he would be when this business had been put through.

"Now, let's sum up the whole goddamn thing," he muttered to himself. "Damn it, where is that cursed pencil again? I had it right between my fingers. Ah, there it is. Ten thousand he ordered. Well, well, there we got a clean-cut profit of fifteen thousand four hundred and forty genuine dollars. Sweet smackers. Fifteen grand right into papa's pocket. Come to think of it, that Republic isn't so backward after all."

"Buenas tardes, mi amigo, how are you?" he greeted the Indian whom he found squatting in the porch of his jacalito as if he had never moved from his place since Mr. Winthrop had left for New York.

The Indian rose, took off his hat, bowed politely and said in his soft voice, "Be welcome, patroncito. Thank you, I feel fine, thank you. Muy buenas tardes. This house and all I have is at your kind disposal." He bowed once more, moved his right hand in a gesture of greeting and sat down again. But he excused himself for doing so by saying, "Perdo-neme, patroncito, I have to take advantage of the daylight, soon it will be night."

"I've got big business for you, my friend," Mr. Winthrop began.

"Good to hear that, señor."

Mr. Winthrop said to himself, "Now, he'll jump up and go wild when he learns what I've got for him." And aloud he said: "Do you think you can make me one thousand of these little baskets?"

"Why not, patroncito? If I can make sixteen, I can make one thousand also."

"That's right, my good man. Can you also make five thousand?"

"Of course, señor. I can make five thousand if I can make one thousand."

"Good. Now, if I should ask you to make me ten thousand, what would you say? And what would be the price of each? You can make ten thousand, can't you?"

"Of course, I can, señor. I can make as many as you wish. You see, I am an expert in this sort of work. No one else in the whole state can make them the way I do."

"That's what I thought and that's exactly why I came to you."

"Thank you for the honor, patroncito."

"Suppose I order you to make me ten thousand of these baskets, how much time do you think you would need to deliver them?"

The Indian, without interrupting his work, cocked his head to one side and then to the other as if he were counting the days or weeks it would cost him to make all these baskets.

After a few minutes he said in a slow voice, "It will take a good long time to make so many baskets, patroncito. You see, the bast and the fibers must be very dry before they can be used properly. Then all during the time they are slowly drying, they must be worked and handled in a very special way so that while drying they won't lose their softness and their flexibility and their natural brilliance. Even when dry they must look fresh. They must never lose their natural properties or they will look just as lifeless and dull as straw. Then while they are drying up I got to get the plants and roots and barks and insects from which I brew the dyes. That takes much time also, believe me. The plants must be gathered when the moon is just right or they won't give the right color. The insects I pick from the plants must also be gathered at the right time and under the right conditions or else they produce no rich colors and are just like dust. But, of course, jefecito, I can make as many of these canastitas[2] as you wish, even as many as three dozens if you want them. Only give me time."

"Three dozens? Three dozens?" Mr. Winthrop yelled, and threw up both arms in desperation. "Three dozens!" he repeated as if he had to say it many times in his own voice so as to understand the real meaning of it, because for a while he thought that he was dreaming. He had expected the Indian to go crazy on hearing that he was to sell ten thousand of his baskets without having to peddle them from door to door and be treated like a dog with a skin disease.

So the American took up the question of price again, by which he hoped to activate the Indian's ambition. "You

---

[2] *canastitas:* little baskets.

told me that if I take one hundred baskets you will let me have them for forty centavos apiece. Is that right, my friend?"

"Quite right, jefecito."

"Now," Mr. Winthrop took a deep breath, "now, then, if I ask you to make me one thousand, that is, ten times one hundred baskets, how much will they cost me, each basket?"

That figure was too high for the Indian to grasp. He became slightly confused and for the first time since Mr. Winthrop had arrived he interrupted his work and tried to think it out. Several times he shook his head and looked vaguely around as if for help. Finally he said, "Excuse me, jefecito, little chief, that is by far too much for me to count. Tomorrow, if you will do me the honor, come and see me again and I think I shall have my answer ready for you, patroncito."

When on the next morning Mr. Winthrop came to the hut he found the Indian as usual squatting on the floor under the overhanging palm roof working at his baskets.

"Have you got the price for ten thousand?" he asked the Indian the very moment he saw him, without taking the trouble to say "Good Morning!"

"Si, patroncito, I have the price ready. You may believe me when I say it has cost me much labor and worry to find out the exact price, because, you see, I do not wish to cheat you out of your honest money."

"Skip that, amigo. Come out with the salad. What's the price?" Mr. Winthrop asked nervously.

"The price is well calculated now without any mistake on my side. If I got to make one thousand canastitas each will be three pesos. If I must make five thousand, each will cost nine pesos. And if I have to make ten thousand, in such a case I can't make them for less than fifteen pesos each." Immediately he returned to his work as if he were afraid of losing too much time with such idle talk.

Mr. Winthrop thought that perhaps it was his faulty knowledge of this foreign language that had played a trick on him.

"Did I hear you say fifteen pesos each if I eventually would buy ten thousand?"

"That's exactly and without any mistake what I've said, patroncito," the Indian answered in his soft courteous voice.

"But now, see here, my good man, you can't do this to me. I'm your friend and I want to help you get on your feet."

"Yes, patroncito, I know this and I don't doubt any of your words."

"Now, let's be patient and talk this over quietly as man to man. Didn't you tell me that if I would buy one hundred you would sell each for forty centavos?"

"Si, jefecito, that's what I said. If you buy one hundred you can have them for forty centavos apiece, provided that I have one hundred, which I don't."

"Yes, yes, I see that." Mr. Winthrop felt as if he would go insane any minute now. "Yes, so you said. Only what I can't comprehend is why you cannot sell at the same price if you make me ten thousand. I certainly don't wish to chisel on the price. I am not that kind. Only, well, let's see now, if you can sell for forty centavos at all, be it for twenty or fifty or a hundred, I can't quite get the idea why the price has to jump that high if I buy more than a hundred."

"Bueno, patroncito, what is there so difficult to understand? It's all very simple. One thousand canastitas cost me a hundred times more work than a dozen. Ten thousand cost me so much time and labor that I could never finish them, not even in a hundred years. For a thousand canastitas

I need more bast than for a hundred, and I need more little red beetles and more plants and roots and bark for the dyes. It isn't that you just can walk into the bush and pick all the things you need at your heart's desire. One root with the true violet blue may cost me four or five days until I can find one in the jungle. And have you thought how much time it costs and how much hard work to prepare the bast and fibers? What is more, if I must make so many baskets, who then will look after my corn and my beans and my goats and chase for me occasionally a rabbit for meat on Sunday? If I have no corn, then I have no tortillas to eat, and if I grow no beans, where do I get my frijoles from?"

"But since you'll get so much money from me for your baskets you can buy all the corn and beans in the world and more than you need."

"That's what you think, señorito, little lordy. But you see, it is only the corn I grow myself that I am sure of. Of the corn which others may or may not grow, I cannot be sure to feast upon."

"Haven't you got some relatives here in this village who might help you to make baskets for me?" Mr. Winthrop asked hopefully.

"Practically the whole village is related to me somehow or other. Fact is, I got lots of close relatives in this here place."

"Why then can't they cultivate your fields and look after your goats while you make baskets for me? Not only this, they might gather for you the fibers and the colors in the bush and lend you a hand here and there in preparing the material you need for the baskets."

"They might, patroncito, yes, they might. Possible. But then you see who would take care of their fields and cattle if they work for me? And if they help me with the baskets it turns out the same. No one would any longer work his fields properly. In such a case corn and beans would get up so high in price that none of us could buy any and we all would starve to death. Besides, as the price of everything would rise and rise higher still how could I make baskets at forty centavos apiece? A pinch of salt or one green chili would set me back more than I'd collect for one single basket. Now you'll understand, highly estimated caballero[3] and jefecito, why I can't make the baskets any cheaper than fifteen pesos each if I got to make that many."

Mr. Winthrop was hard-boiled, no wonder considering the city he came from. He refused to give up the more than fifteen thousand dollars which at that moment seemed to slip through his fingers like nothing. Being really desperate now, he talked and bargained with the Indian for almost two full hours, trying to make him understand how rich he, the Indian, would become if he would take this greatest opportunity of his life.

The Indian never ceased working on his baskets while he explained his points of view.

"You know, my good man," Mr. Winthrop said, "such a wonderful chance might never again knock on your door, do you realize that? Let me explain to you in ice-cold figures what fortune you might miss if you leave me flat on this deal."

He tore out leaf after leaf from his notebook, covered each with figures and still more figures, and while doing so told the peasant he would be the richest man in the whole district.

The Indian without answering watched with a genuine

---

[3] *caballero:* gentleman.

expression of awe as Mr. Winthrop wrote down these long figures, executing complicated multiplications and divisions and subtractions so rapidly that it seemed to him the greatest miracle he had ever seen.

The American, noting this growing interest in the Indian, misjudged the real significance of it. "There you are, my friend," he said. "That's exactly how rich you're going to be. You'll have a bankroll of exactly four thousand pesos. And to show you that I'm a real friend of yours, I'll throw in a bonus. I'll make it a round five thousand pesos, and all in silver."

The Indian, however, had not for one moment thought of four thousand pesos. Such an amount of money had no meaning to him. He had been interested solely in Mr. Winthrop's ability to write figures so rapidly.

"So, what do you say now? Is it a deal or is it? Say yes and you'll get your advance this very minute."

"As I have explained before, patroncito, the price is fifteen pesos each."

"But, my good man," Mr. Winthrop shouted at the poor Indian in utter despair, "where have you been all this time? On the moon or where? You are still at the same price as before."

"Yes, I know that, jefecito, my little chief," the Indian answered, entirely unconcerned. "It must be the same price because I cannot make any other one. Besides, señor, there's still another thing which perhaps you don't know. You see, my good lordy and caballero, I've to make these canastitas my own way and with my song in them and with bits of my soul woven into them. If I were to make them in great numbers there would no longer be my soul in each, or my songs. Each would look like the other with no difference whatever and such a thing would slowly eat up my heart.

Each has to be another song which I hear in the morning when the sun rises and when the birds begin to chirp and the butterflies come and sit down on my baskets so that I may see a new beauty, because, you see, the butterflies like my baskets and the pretty colors on them, that's why they come and sit down, and I can make my canastitas after them. And now, señor jefecito, if you will kindly excuse me, I have wasted much time already, although it was a pleasure and a great honor to hear the talk of such a distinguished caballero like you. But I'm afraid I've to attend to my work now, for day after tomorrow is market day in town and I got to take my baskets there. Thank you, señor, for your visit. Adiós."

And in this way it happened that American garbage cans escaped the fate of being turned into receptacles for empty, torn, and crumpled little multicolored canastitas into which an Indian of Mexico had woven dreams of his soul, throbs of his heart: his unsung poems.

Discussion

1. During their first conversation, the Indian showed not the "slightest trace of enthusiasm" as Mr. Winthrop explored the prospects of buying all the baskets he had in stock. Why do you think the Indian acted this way?

2. In reference to the ten thousand baskets that Mr. Winthrop requests, the Indian says, "If I were to make them in great numbers there would no longer be my soul in each, or my songs. Each would look like the other with no difference whatever and such a thing would slowly eat up my heart." What does he mean?

3. How do you think Mr. Winthrop will explain to Mr. Kemple in New York his failure to produce the promised baskets?

4. What has Mr. Winthrop learned from this experience?

Roundtable Discussion

1. Think about the main character in each of the stories you have just read. Which character has learned most about what is really valuable? Which has learned least? Explain your answers.

2. Think about the sacrifices that many of the characters in these stories made for someone else. Do you consider these to be true sacrifices? Explain your answer.

3. For which character do you feel the most sympathy? For which do you feel the least sympathy? Explain your answers.

4. From the experiences of the characters in these stories, what have you learned about values?

The Road Not Taken

Two roads diverged in a yellow wood,
And sorry I could not travel both
And be one traveler, long I stood
And looked down one as far as I could
To where it bent in the undergrowth;

Then took the other, as just as fair,
And having perhaps the better claim,
Because it was grassy and wanted wear;
Though as for that the passing there
Had worn them really about the same,

And both that morning equally lay
In leaves no step had trodden black.
Oh, I kept the first for another day!
Yet knowing how way leads on to way,
I doubted if I should ever come back.

I shall be telling this with a sigh
Somewhere ages and ages hence:
Two roads diverged in a wood, and I—
I took the one less traveled by,
And that has made all the difference.

Robert Frost

About the Authors

Guy de Maupassant Considered one of the world's best short story writers, de Maupassant was born in France in 1850. His parents separated when he was eleven, and the young boy lived with his mother. Through her, he met many writers and artists who later had a great influence on his writing career. Although he wrote many novels, de Maupassant is best remembered for his more than two hundred and fifty short stories. Guy de Maupassant's career was cut short when he died in 1893 at the age of 43.

O. Henry William Sydney Porter, better known by his pen name O. Henry, grew up in North Carolina. He was born in Greensboro in 1862. Later he moved to Texas, where he worked as a bank clerk for a while. His real interest, however, was writing. He soon got a job on a newspaper and began to write the short stories that were to make him famous. Then, Porter was accused of stealing money from the bank where he had worked. He fled the country but, on his return, was captured and sent to prison for three years. In later years, his innocence was finally proved and his name cleared. O. Henry spent the last part of his life in New York, writing. He died there in 1910.

Jesse Stuart "I was born in this wonderful country," Jesse Stuart wrote. "Here I grew from boyhood to manhood." The wonderful country he wrote of was Greenup County, Kentucky, where Stuart was born in 1907. His home was so remote from city life that young Jesse never saw a telephone or an electric light until he was over fifteen. The son of a farmer, Stuart often stayed out of school to help support his family by working on neighboring farms for twenty-five or thirty cents a day. Many of his stories are about incidents from his boyhood. After working his way through college, Stuart became a teacher and superintendent of Greenup County schools.

His efforts to provide better education for the county children sometimes met with lawsuits and threats of violence. Stuart described that time in his life in *The Thread That Runs So True*. Stuart continued to teach and write for most of his life. He died in 1984.

B. Traven Much of B. Traven's life is a mystery. Since Traven did not like to talk about himself in public, little is known about his life. It is believed he was born in Chicago in 1890. His real name was Berik Traven Torsvan. At an early age, he went to work, running errands, shining shoes, and delivering papers. He learned by ear the languages and dialects he heard spoken by Chicago's immigrants. This knowledge proved useful when Traven began his writing career. His best-known book in this country is *The Treasure of the Sierra Madre*. It later became a movie that was almost as famous as the book. It is believed that Traven moved to Mexico sometime around 1920. After that, he became even more of a figure of mystery. It is believed that he died in 1969.

Robert Frost Born in San Francisco in 1874, Robert Frost is the only American to be awarded the Pulitzer Prize four times. Although born in the West, Frost set most of his poems in a rural New England countryside. In 1960, Congress voted Frost a gold medal in recognition of his poetry. One of Frost's last public appearances occurred in 1961, when he read his poem "The Gift Outright" at the inauguration of President John F. Kennedy. Frost died in 1963.

Glossary

a·ban·don (ə **băn′** dən) *n.* An action, condition, or manner of relaxed or reckless carelessness: *The energetic girl played her harmonica with wild abandon.*

ac·ti·vate (**ăk′** tə vāt′) *v.* To make active; set in operation or motion: *I will activate the emergency alarm system during the fire drill.*

ap·per·tain (ăp′ ər **tān′**) *v.* To belong as a function or part; have relation: *The problems that appertain to career choices were addressed at the meeting.*

ar·dent (**är′** dnt) *adj.* Full of warmth of passion, emotion, or desire; passionate: *Her ardent admirer sent her flowers every day.*

a·skew (ə **skyoo′**) *adv. & adj.* Out of line; crooked; awry: *She straightened the picture that was askew.*

askew

as·ser·tion (ə **sûr′** shən) *n.* **1.** The act of declaring a positive statement. **2.** A positive statement or claim, especially one for which no proof is offered: *His assertion was later proven to be false.*

av·o·ca·tion (ăv′ ə **kā′** shən) *n.* An activity engaged in, usually for pleasure, in addition to one's regular work: *The lawyer plays the bassoon as an avocation.*

a·vow (ə **vou′**) *v.* To acknowledge openly; admit freely.

awe (ô) *n.* A feeling of wonder, fear, and respect inspired by something mighty or majestic: *She stood very still, gazing in awe at the mountains.*

bast (băst) *n.* The strong, fibrous part of certain plant stems, used for making rope or cord.

beg·gar (**běg′** ər) *v.* **1.** To make very poor; ruin. **2.** —**beggar description.** To be impossible to describe: *The priceless paintings beggar description.*

ben·e·fi·cial (běn′ ə **f ĭsh′** əl) *adj.* Bringing benefit; advanta-

---

ă pat / ā pay / â care / ä father / ě pet / ē be / ĭ pit / ī pie / î fierce / ŏ pot / ō go / ô paw, for / oi oil / ŏŏ book / o͞o boot / ou out / ŭ cut / û fur / *th* the / th thin / hw which / zh vision / ə ago, item, pencil, atom, circus

geous: *His good advice was beneficial to us.*

bou·doir (**boo′** dwär′) *or* (-dwôr′) *n.* A woman's private sitting room or dressing room.

boun·ti·ful (**boun′** tə fəl) *adj.* **1.** Generous. **2.** Plentiful; abundant: *The fishermen were happy to come upon a stream bountiful with trout.*

breech·es (**brĭch′** ĭz) *n. pl.* Short fitted trousers ending at or just below the knees: *Wearing breeches didn't keep my legs warm.*

can·de·la·brum (kăn′ dl ä′ brəm) *n., pl.* **can·de·la·bra** (kăn′ dl ä′ brə) *or* **can·de·la·brums.** A large decorative candlestick with several arms or branches for holding candles.

candlelabra

caste (kăst) *n.* **1.** In India, one of the hereditary social classes of the Hindus. **2.** Any social class distinguished by rank, profession, or other position in a system: *The poor family thought it unfair that it couldn't escape its caste.*

ca·tas·tro·phe (kə tăs′ trə fē) *n.* A great and sudden calamity; disaster: *A combination of unexpected events made the summit meeting a catastrophe.*

cu·ri·o (**kyoor′** ē ō′) *n.* A rare or unusual object of art: *He collects old china figurines and other such curios.*

del·i·ca·cy (**dĕl′** ĭ kə sē) *n.* Fineness of structure, quality, texture, or form; daintiness: *She showed great delicacy in her gentle manner.*

di·lem·ma (dĭ **lĕm′** ə) *n.* A situation that requires a person to choose between courses of action that are equally difficult or unpleasant: *The dilemma he faced was whether he should tell the authorities what he knew.*

dis·creet (dĭ **skrēt′**) *adj.* Having or showing caution or self-restraint in one's speech or behavior; showing good judgment; prudent: *I can trust my discreet friend with any secret.*

dow·ry (**dou′** rē) *n.* Money or property brought by a bride to

---

ă pat / ā **pay** / â care / ä father / ĕ pet / ē be / ĭ pit / ī pie / î fierce / ŏ pot / ō go / ô **paw,** for / oi oil / ŏŏ book / ōō boot / ou out / ŭ cut / û fur / th **the** / th thin / hw **wh**ich / zh vision / ə ago, item, pencil, atom, circus

her husband: *The man marveled at his future wife's large dowry, which included some real estate.*

du·pli·ca·tion (doo′ plĭ kā′ shən) *or* (dyoo-) *n.* The condition of two things being exactly alike or replicas of each other: *Lack of planning resulted in duplication of effort.*

dy·nam·ic (dī **năm′** ĭk) *adj.* Energetic; vigorous: *The audience roared after the dancer's dynamic performance.*

ev·i·dent (ĕv′ ĭ dənt) *adj.* Obvious; clear; plain: *His unhappiness became evident when he started to cry.*

ex·ot·ic (ĭg **zŏt′** ĭk) *adj.* **1.** From another part of the world; foreign. **2.** Having the charm of the unfamiliar; strikingly or intriguingly unusual: *The exotic dinner was flavored with unusual spices.*

ex·ploit (ĭk **sploit′**) *v.* **1.** To make the greatest possible use of; turn to advantage. **2.** To make use of selfishly or unethically: *The forests were exploited for all their timber.*

ex·qui·site (ĕk′ skwĭz ĭt) *or* (ĭk **skwĭz′** ĭt) *adj.* Of special beauty, charm, elegance, or taste: *The stylish lady had exquisite taste in clothes.*

freak (frēk) *n.***1.** A markedly abnormal person or animal. **2.** A thing or occurrence that is very unusual or irregular: *A freak accident occurred when lightning struck his car.*

hewed (hyood) *adj.* Made or shaped with an ax or knife.

hu·mil·i·at·ing (hyoo **mĭl′** ē ā tĭng) *adj.* Lowering the pride or status of; humbled or disgraced: *Having to make a public apology was most humiliating for him.*

im·pu·ta·tion (ĭm′ pyoo tā′ shən) *n.* The act of attributing (a crime or fault) to a cause or source: *The coach rejected the imputation that poor guidance led to a bad season.*

in·con·se·quen·tial (ĭn kŏn′ sĭ **kwĕn′** shəl) *adj.* Without significance; lacking importance; petty: *The class staged an inconsequential and boring debate.*

in·trin·sic (ĭn **trĭn′** sĭk) *adj.* Being part of the basic nature of a thing; fundamental; essential: *She is respected by everyone for her intrinsic honesty.* **—in·trin′ si·cal·ly** *adv.*

mam·moth (**măm′** əth) *adj.* Huge; gigantic: *The under-*

ground explosion left a mammoth hole in the ground.

ma·ture (mə to͞or′) *or* (-tyo͞or′) *or* (-cho͞or′) *v*. **1.** To reach full growth or development. **2.** To become ripe: *The apples are maturing, and will be ready to pick soon.*

men·di·can·cy (mĕn′ dĭ kən sē) *n*. The act of begging.

mer·e·tri·cious (mĕr′ ĭ trĭsh′ əs) *adj*. Attracting attention by cheap or false means; showy; gaudy: *I prefer simple design to meretricious ornamentation.*

nim·ble (nĭm′ bəl) *adj*. Moving or able to move quickly, lightly, and easily; agile: *Her nimble fingers worked the piano keys with remarkable speed.*

par·si·mo·ny (pär′ sə mō′ nē) *n*. Extreme or excessive reluctance to spend money or use resources; stinginess: *The miser's parsimony was so great that she refused to spend money on food.*

pat·ent (păt′ nt) *adj*. Obvious; plain: *His patent lie didn't fool anyone.*

pet·tish (pĕt′ ĭsh) *adj*. Ill-tempered; peevish: *The tired and hungry baby is in a pettish mood.* —**pet′tish·ly** *adv*.

pit·tance (pĭt′ ns) *n*. A small allowance of money: *The struggling artist lived on a mere pittance.*

plun·der (plŭn′ dər) *n*. **1.** Stolen property; booty. **2.** In some regions, personal goods and property.

ply (plī) *v*. To traverse (a route or course) regularly: *The ferries ply between the islands on a weekly schedule.*

pre·dom·i·nate (prĭ dŏm′ ə nāt′) *v*. To be greater than others in strength, number, importance, or prominence: *Reds and yellows are predominating in this season's fashions.*

pri·va·tion (prī vā′ shən) *n*. Lack of the basic necessities or comforts of life: *Privations of food and shelter caused despair.*

pru·dence (pro͞od′ ns) *n*. The quality of being cautious or sensible; good judgment: *She showed prudence by thinking before speaking.*

quaint (kwānt) *adj*. Old fashioned, especially in a pleasing

---

ă pat / ā pay / â care / ä father / ĕ pet / ē be / ĭ pit / ī pie / î fierce / ŏ pot / ō go / ô paw, for / oi oil / o͝o book / o͞o boot / ou out / ŭ cut / û fur / th the / th thin / hw which / zh vision / ə ago, item, pencil, atom, circus

way: *The absence of traffic lights was charming in the quaint little town.*

ru·in·ous (**rōō′** ə nəs) *adj.* Causing or likely to cause ruin; disastrous: *The agreement seemed good at first but brought on ruinous results.*

scru·ti·ny (**skrōōt′** n ē) *n.* A close, careful look or study: *Sammy fidgeted under the cold, silent scrutiny of the teacher.*

ster·ling (**stûr′** lĭng) *adj.* **1.** Of or expressed in British money. **2.** Of the highest quality; very fine: *Her sterling qualifications made finding a good job very easy.*

throb (thrŏb) *n.* A beat or pounding, as of the heart: *His heart beat so hard that he thought everyone could hear its throbs.*

tru·ant (**trōō′** ənt) *adj.* Absent without permission: *The truant student was caught in the playground during class time.*

u·nique (yōō **nēk′**) *adj.* **1.** Being the only one. **2.** Having no equal or equivalent; being the only one in kind or excellence: *That kind of unique opportunity comes around only once in a lifetime.*

ur·ban·i·ty (ûr′ **băn′** ə tē) *n.* Refinement and elegance of manners; polished courtesy.

va·grant (**vā′** grənt) *n.* A person who wanders from place to place and usually has no means of support; a tramp; vagabond: *The vagrant always slept in the same alleyway.*

ves·ti·bule (**věs′** tə byōōl′) *n.* A small entrance hall or lobby: *The mail boxes are in the vestibule.*